Stuttering: Straight Talk for Teachers

A Handbook for Teachers and Speech-Language Pathologists

THE STUTTERING FOUNDATION®
PUBLICATION NO. 0125

Produced and written by Lisa Scott, Ph.D., The Florida State University and Carroll Guitar, M.L.S., University of Vermont; in collaboration with Kristin Chmela, M.A., adjunct faculty, Northwestern University; Jane Fraser, President, The Stuttering Foundation; and Bill Murphy, M.A., Purdue University. In collaboration with Joseph Denaker, M.A., Children's Hospital of Philadelphia and Lee Caggiano, M.A., private practice.

Stuttering:
Straight Talk for Teachers
A Handbook for Teachers and
Speech-Language Pathologists
Publication No. 0125

First Edition – 2002
Second Printing – 2003
Second Edition – 2005
Second Printing – 2006

Published by:
The Stuttering Foundation
3100 Walnut Grove Road, Suite 603
Post Office Box 11749
Memphis, TN 38111-0749

ISBN 0-933388-50-1

The Stuttering Foundation is a nonprofit charitable organization dedicated to the prevention and improved treatment of stuttering. Contributions are tax-deductible.

Printed in the United States of America

Section I
For Teachers

Stuttering is a communication disorder that interferes with a person's ability to speak fluently. It involves the repetition, prolongation, or blockage of sounds, syllables, or words.

When a child stutters, his academic performance and social life may be affected: he may hesitate to raise his hand in class, read aloud, or talk with other children in the class. This handbook is designed to give you practical information about stuttering and to suggest strategies that may help you better meet the needs of the children in your class.

This handbook contains:

1. General information about stuttering;
2. A checklist for making a referral to a speech-language pathologist (SLP) if you are concerned a child in your class may be stuttering;
3. Answers to questions you may have about stuttering;
4. An overview of what happens in speech therapy for stuttering;
5. Suggestions regarding information you can share with the SLP;
6. Suggestions for sharing information with parents;
7. Brief descriptions of various resources on stuttering, teasing, and building self-esteem in children. Some of these resources are geared for teachers, some for children, and others for parents. A brief explanation of each resource accompanies its listing.

General Information About Stuttering

This section addresses general information about stuttering, including causes of stuttering, facts about stuttering, what stuttering looks like, and how children may feel about stuttering.

Causes

- Stuttering usually begins between the ages of two and four. While there is no known cause of stuttering, researchers agree that it likely results from an interaction of factors including child development, family dynamics, genetics, and neurophysiology.

Facts About Stuttering

- More boys stutter than girls. At age two, the ratio is approximately two boys for every girl but by fifth grade, approximately four boys will stutter for each girl.
- Approximately 5 percent of all children go through a period of stuttering that lasts six months or more. Three-quarters of those will recover by late childhood, leaving about 1% with a long-term problem.
- If a child has been stuttering longer than three years, however, it is very unlikely she will outgrow it. Because most children begin stuttering during their preschool years, a child who stutters in elementary, middle, or high school is much less likely to outgrow the problem.
- There is no known cure for stuttering, including speech therapy. Instead, speech therapy helps the child learn to talk in an easier manner, even quite fluently, and to have healthy attitudes and feelings about talking.
- Stuttering is not caused by psychological differences. Children do not begin stuttering because they are more anxious, more shy, or more depressed than other children.
- Children who stutter show no differences in intelligence from children who don't stutter.
- The amount of stuttering heard in a child's speech will vary across speaking situations and partners. For example, a child may not stutter at all when speaking to friends but will stutter more when reading aloud in class.
- Stuttering can be cyclical, meaning that it comes and goes. The frequency and severity of a child's stuttering can change dramatically across a period of several weeks or months.
- Children who stutter may be self-conscious about their stuttering and choose not to participate in class.
- Many famous and successful people stutter. Well-known people who stutter include James Earl Jones, John Stossel, Kenyon Martin, Annie Glenn, Bill Walton, Mel Tillis, Nicholas Brendon, Robert Merrill, Carly Simon, Ken Venturi, Bob Love, John Updike, Lewis Carroll, King George VI, Winston Churchill and Marilyn Monroe. The Stuttering Foundation brochure, *16 Famous People Who Stutter:* National Stuttering Awareness Week, depicts these famous people.

Additional facts about stuttering can be found in The Stuttering Foundation® fact sheet, *Did You Know: A Fact Sheet About Stuttering,* also in this handbook on page 19.

What Stuttering Looks and Sounds Like

Stuttering usually occurs on the beginning sounds or words in a sentence, or at clause boundaries. There are three main patterns of stuttering. You may hear the child in your class stuttering in only one of these ways; others will show considerable variety in stuttering patterns.

1. *Repetitions of sounds and syllables.* The child will usually repeat the sound or syllable three times or more.

   M-m-m-may I go to the bathroom?

   I-I-I-I know the answer!

2. *Sound prolongations.* You will hear the child "holding onto" the sound as he tries to say it.

   Sssssscience is interesting.

   Eeeeeeeeven though the book was hard to read, I liked it.

3. *Blocks.* When a child is blocking on a sound, you may see her trying to say the word but not hear any sound coming out of her mouth. This period of silence is often followed by a quick burst of sound when she is finally able to say the word.

It's also common to hear a child use "um," or "uh," as he struggles to get speech going, or changes in pitch or loudness as he tries to say a stuttered word.

In addition to the stuttering you hear, you may see the child closing her eyes or her lips, cheeks, or jaw becoming very tense during stuttering. Some children even tap their fingers or feet, or move their bodies in other ways while trying to say an especially difficult word. These behaviors, called secondary or accessory behaviors, usually occur because the child is trying to force the word out.

How Children May Feel About Stuttering

Some children who stutter do not have any negative feelings associated with talking, but others may feel frustrated, anxious, embarrassed, or even ashamed. It's important to know that a child's feelings about talking may not be related at all to *how much* he stutters. That is, a child you observe to stutter frequently and severely may not feel bad at all about talking in class, whereas another child whose stuttering seems very mild may feel anxious and afraid.

If a child has negative feelings about talking, he may be unwilling to raise his hand, pretend that he doesn't know an answer when called on, or withdraw from social situations such as sitting with others at lunch or playing with a group on the playground.

Should You Make a Referral?

You may have ordered this video and handbook because you're concerned that a child in your class may be stuttering. The Teacher's Referral Checklist in Table 1 on the next page can help you decide.

Also, talk with the child's parents to find out whether they're concerned, and whether the child has ever had a speech evaluation or been in speech therapy. Questions you may want to ask parents include:

- Have you noticed your child repeat parts of words rather than whole words or phrases? (For example, "a-a-a-apple")
- Do you hear your child repeat sounds more than once every 8 or 10 sentences?
- When you hear your child repeat, do you hear more than two repetitions? (For example, "a-a-a-a-a-apple" instead of "a-a-apple")
- Does your child seem frustrated or embarrassed when he has trouble with a word?
- Has your child talked like this for more than a year?
- Have you ever noticed your child raise the pitch of his voice, blink his eyes, look away, or have muscle tension in his face when he stutters?
- Does he use extra words or sounds like "uh" or "um" or "well" to get a word started?
- Does your child sometimes get stuck so badly that no sound at all comes out?
- Have you ever noticed your child use extra body movements, like tapping his finger, to get sounds out?
- Do you think your child ever avoids talking, substitutes words, or quits talking in the middle of a sentence because he might stutter?

These questions are listed in order of the seriousness of the problem. If a parent answers "yes" to any question other than number 1, it suggests the possibility of stuttering rather than normal disfluency. Together with the parent, you can decide whether to make a referral to a speech-language pathologist.

TABLE 1:

Teacher's Check list for Referral

	Probably Normal Disfluencies	Probably Stuttering
Speech behavior you may see or hear:	☐ Occasional (less than once every 10 sentences), brief (less than 1/2 second), repetitions of sounds, syllables, or short words li-like this. Sounds, syllables, or words only repeated once or twice, for example hey-hey, ca-ca-can.	☐ Frequent (3 or more every 10 sentences), long (longer than 1/2 second) repetitions of sounds, syllables, and some short words, li-li-li-like this. Sounds, syllables, and short words usually repeated 3 or more times, f-f-f-f-for ex-ex-ex-example. Occasional prolongation of sounds lllllike this, or blockages.
Other behavior you may see or hear:	☐ Occasional pauses, hesitations in speech, or fillers such as "uh," "er," or "um," usually noticed when the child is changing words or thoughts.	☐ Repetitions and prolongations may be associated with eyelid closing and blinking, looking away, and some muscle tension in and around the mouth. May also hear changes in pitch or loudness as child struggles to say word. Child may say extra sounds or words as starters, e.g., "Well it's well it's I-I-I-I need a crayon."
When problem is most noticeable:	☐ Tends to come and go when child is: tired, excited, talking about complex or new topic, asking or answering questions, or talking to unresponsive listeners.	☐ May come and go in similar situations, but is more often present than absent. If noticed in most speaking situations and is consistent, problem may be more severe.
Child's reaction:	☐ None apparent	☐ May show concern, embarrassment, frustration, fear of speaking. May be reluctant to participate in classroom activities such as show-and-tell, reading aloud, or raising hand during question-answer periods.
Peer reactions:	☐ None apparent	☐ May show concern, embarrassment, frustration, fear of speaking. May be reluctant to participate in classroom activities such as show-and-tell, reading aloud, or raising hand during question-answer periods.
Parent reactions:	☐ None to a great deal	☐ Some degree of concern
Referral decision	☐ No referral	☐ Refer for screening

Questions Teachers Often Have About Stuttering

What should I do when a child stutters in my class?

The most important thing to do when a child is stuttering is to be a good communicator yourself.

- Keep eye contact and give the child enough time to finish speaking.
- Try not to fill in words or sentences.
- Let the child know by your manner and actions that you are listening to what she says—not how she says it.
- Model wait time—taking two seconds before you answer a child's question—and insert more pauses into your own speech to help reduce speech pressure.

These suggestions will benefit all of the children in your class.

Do not make remarks like "slow down," "take a deep breath," "relax," or "think about what you're going to say, then say it." We often say these things to children because slowing down, relaxing, or thinking about what we are going to say helps us when we feel like we're having a problem tripping over our words. Stuttering, though, is a different kind of speaking problem; and this kind of advice is simply not helpful to the child who stutters.

Should I remind the child to use his stuttering therapy techniques in class?

Unless the child or an SLP specifically asks you to help remind the child, it may be best not to.

In therapy, children who stutter learn several different techniques, sometimes called speech tools, to manage their stuttering. However, learning to use these speech tools in different situations (e.g., the classroom vs. the therapy room) takes considerable time and practice. Many young children who stutter do not have the maturity to monitor their speech in all situations. Therefore, it may be unrealistic to expect the child to use her tools in your classroom.

What should I do when the child is having a difficult speaking day?

It's always best to check with the child about what he would like you to do on days when talking is more difficult.

Children who stutter vary greatly in how they want their teachers and peers to respond when they are having an especially difficult time talking. One child may prefer that his teacher treat him in the same way as she would any other day, by spontaneously calling on him or asking him to read aloud.

On the other hand, another child may want his teacher to temporarily reduce her expectations for his verbal participation, by calling on him only if his hand is raised or allowing him to take a pass during activities such as round-robin reading.

What should I do when the child who stutters interrupts another child?

Handle interruptions the same way that you would for a child who doesn't stutter. Children who stutter sometimes interrupt others because it's easier to get speech going while others are talking. We're not sure exactly why it's easier to talk over others, but it may be because less attention is called to the child at the beginning of her turn when stuttering is most likely to occur.

Even though it may be easier to get her speech going by interrupting a peer, it's important for the child who stutters to learn the rules for good communication just like all the other children in your class.

How can I make oral reports easier for the stuttering child?

There are many things you can do to help make oral reports a positive experience for the child who stutters. Together, you and the child can develop a plan, considering factors such as:

- Order—whether he wants to be one of the first to present, in the middle, or one of the last to present;
- Practice opportunities—ways he can practice that will help him feel more comfortable, such as at home, with you, with a friend, or at a speech therapy session;
- Audience size—whether to give the oral report in private, in a small group, or in front of the entire class; and
- Other issues—whether he should be timed, or whether grading criteria should be modified because of his stuttering.

Should I talk to the entire class about stuttering?

It depends on the child in question. Some children won't mind if you talk to their peers about stuttering. Others, however, will feel that stuttering is a private matter and should not be discussed openly with the other children in class.

Sometimes, a child who stutters will make a classroom presentation about stuttering. This presentation allows the child to teach her peers facts about stuttering, give them names of famous people who stutter, offer suggestions about how she would like her peers to react when she is stuttering, and even teach the others different ways to stutter.

One of the benefits we've observed from having a child who stutters make a classroom presentation about stuttering is a reduction in teasing. If other children understand more about the problem, they are less likely to ridicule or tease the child who stutters.

This is not an appropriate activity for all children who stutter, as some may not be ready yet to deal with stuttering in such an open way. Giving a presentation about stuttering is one component of stuttering therapy, typically done in conjunction with a classroom visit by the SLP. If you have questions about whether the child in your class is ready to give such a presentation, consult the SLP.

If a child in your class is going to make a presentation about stuttering, The Stuttering Foundation has a Classroom Presentation Packet (#0130) with brochures, information, and posters you and the child can use.

How should I handle teasing?

Deal with teasing in the child who stutters just as you would with any other child who is being teased. Unfortunately, teasing is an experience common to many children.

As mentioned earlier, classroom presentations can be a powerful way to reduce teasing if the child who stutters is ready to make such a presentation.

At other times, teasing will be stopped only with your intervention. Many school districts now have written policies for handling teasing in the classroom, and school counselors or social workers are excellent sources of information.

A book with humorous and practical suggestions for teasing is *Bullies Are a Pain in the Brain,* by T. Romain of Free Spirit Publishing. Additional resources for children, teachers, and parents can be found at the end of this handbook.

Here are some other suggestions:

1. Listen to the child and provide support right away. Don't dismiss teasing with a remark such as "Everybody does it."
2. Discuss problem solving and coping strategies for teasing and bullying with the child and choose several that suit him or her. These problem solving skills and coping strategies may also have been a part of speech therapy.
3. Educate others. The more others know about stuttering, the less likely they will be to tease.
4. Talk with the class about teasing and bullying in general. The child who stutters is probably not the only one being bullied or teased.
5. Talk with parents, the speech pathologist, and other teachers so that you are all on the same page.

What types of things can I say to encourage the child who stutters to talk in my class?

The best way to encourage a child who stutters to talk in your class is to let him know through your words and actions that what he says is important, not the way he says it. Other ways you can encourage the child:

- Praise him for sharing his ideas;
- Tell him that stuttering does not bother you;
- Give him opportunities to talk, such as calling on him to give an answer or asking him for his opinion; and,
- Let him know it's OK to stutter.

You may have other general questions about stuttering, the child who stutters in your class, or what to say to parents of children who stutter. We encourage you to contact the SLP in your building. If you don't have a SLP in your building or access to one through your school system, contact The Stuttering Foundation for more information.

What Happens in Stuttering Therapy

Goals of stuttering therapy

There are usually two main goals in stuttering therapy:

- Making talking easier, and
- Developing healthier attitudes and feelings about talking.

Making talking easier is achieved by teaching children speech tools. These tools help the child produce speech in a different way, such as reducing the amount of tension in the speech system, beginning a sentence with more air, or stuttering in an easier way.

Developing healthier attitudes and feelings about talking is achieved by helping the child learn to respond to speaking situations with less anxiety, become more confident in his ability to use these speech tools, and use problem solving skills for difficult speaking situations.

Not all children need to change how they feel about talking. Many are confident and willingly talk to others. For some, however, talking can produce feelings of anxiety or fear, even guilt and shame. Overcoming these negative attitudes and feelings can be just as important for the child as learning to talk more easily.

Talking more fluently is only one part of being a good communicator. Learning to take turns, not interrupt, and using eye contact when speaking are also important communication skills. Sometimes, the harder a child tries to use his tools and be fluent, the more he will stutter. Again, it's important to let children know that they shouldn't be ashamed to stutter, it's OK to stutter.

Stuttering: For Kids By Kids is a wonderful way for younger children to learn more and to meet other kids who stutter.

For more information on what happens in speech therapy, two Stuttering Foundation videos/DVDs may be of interest to you or the child in your class who stutters. *Therapy in Action: The School-Age Child Who Stutters* focuses on elementary-age children, and *Stuttering: Straight Talk for Teens* is for adolescents. More information about these tapes can be found in the Resources section at the end of this handbook.

Why children may not use speech tools all the time

For any of us, learning to change the way we talk is very difficult. Think about times you've had to try to slow down or use a different style of speaking, and then consider whether you'd be able to do this in all situations with all listeners!

Being expected to use speech tools consistently can be especially difficult for a child who stutters. Possible reasons she may be unable or unwilling to use her tools include:

- being excited or rushed;
- feeling tired or sick; or,
- having difficulty with the language demands of the speaking situation, such as having to give an especially long or complex answer.
- being unsure about how to use her speech tools;

How we talk is something people who do not stutter give very little attention. One example of exactly how difficult making this type of change may be is to practice writing your signature with your opposite hand. We often use this activity with children as part of a classroom presentation about stuttering or with parents of children who stutter. After trying to write with the opposite hand, we ask:

- How much did you have to think about writing with your other hand?
- Did it feel natural?
- Does your signature look the way it normally would?

Responses usually include that signing with the opposite hand took a great deal of thought, felt very unnatural because of changes in the angle of the pen or the amount of pressure applied to the paper, and did not look at all like the person's typical signature.

We then make the analogy that this is how it feels to change speech: it takes concentration, it feels unnatural, and it sounds different. These are additional reasons children may hesitate to use their speech tools.

Changes to expect from speech therapy

Speech therapy can be a long-term process. Children may show changes in both *how they talk* and *how they feel* about talking as they learn to successfully manage their stuttering. As a result of speech therapy, you may notice the child:

- becoming more fluent;
- stuttering with less tension;
- using more eye contact;
- volunteering to answer questions rather than only answering when called on;
- contributing ideas during a brainstorming session;
- talking more with peers; or
- changing how and when he talks in other ways.

Sharing Information with Speech-Language Pathologists

If you have a child who stutters in your class, your insights about the child and his communication skills are valuable to the speech therapist. However, like you, many SLPs are busy and may not see the need to schedule a meeting to talk specifically about the child.

Nonetheless, your input is **critical.** Consider sharing information with the SLP through a meeting, e-mail or a written note, regarding:

- Your observations about how this child learns best in your classroom;

- The child's academic performance, and whether you feel it is affected by stuttering;

    Does he voluntarily raise his hand in class?

    Does he volunteer to read out loud?

    Does he participate in show-and-tell or give oral reports?

    Does he participate in cooperative learning activities?

- Her social relationships and whether you feel they are affected by her stuttering;

    Does she seem to have many friends?

    Is she being teased about her stuttering?

    Does she interrupt or not allow other children a turn to talk?

    Do other children treat her differently because of her stuttering, or do they treat her as "one of the gang"?

- Any questions you may have about ...

    the child's stuttering and other communication skills;

    the child's speech therapy;

    stuttering in general.

Sharing Information with Parents

Parents may have many questions for you about their child and how his stuttering affects him in the classroom. For example, they may want to know whether you see the child participating in class, whether his peers are teasing him, or they may have basic questions about stuttering. If the child is not currently in speech therapy, his parents may also want to know how to get help for stuttering.

When you meet with the child's parents, consider discussing the same kinds of information found in the previous section on sharing information with SLPs. Talk with parents in an open, honest way about how you see stuttering affecting the child. Many times, your insights will provide the reassurance they need to feel confident that his stuttering is not a problem for him at school. However, if you are concerned, the information and examples you can provide can help parents make a decision about getting help for their child.

On the next page, you'll find a list of suggestions for parents of children who stutter. You can copy this page and give it to parents.

If you feel the parents need additional information about stuttering, encourage them to contact the speech-language pathologist in your building. If there isn't a therapist in your building, you can copy the information in this handbook or contact The Stuttering Foundation at 1-800-992-9392 or www.stutteringhelp.org (www.tartamudez.org in Spanish).

The Stuttering Foundation sends a free packet of information to parents, and the Web site has a wealth of resources for them. The Foundation publishes several books, videos and DVDs specifically for parents including *Stuttering For Kids By Kids* (DVD #0172, VHS #0170); *If Your Child Stutters: A Guide for Parents* (6th edition, book #0011); *Stuttering and Your Child: Questions and Answers* (3rd edition, book #0022); and *Stuttering and Your Child: Help for Families* (DVD #0073) which is helpful for children of all ages, and *Stuttering and Your Child: A Videotape for Parents* (video #0075)

In addition, over 6,000 public libraries have copies of Stuttering Foundation books, DVDs and tapes available for check-out free of charge. For a list of these libraries, go to the Foundation's Web site at www.stutteringhelp.org, click on the Resources button, and then on the link for Library Lists.

7 tips for talking with your child

1. **Speak with your child in an unhurried way, pausing frequently.** Wait a few seconds after your child finishes speaking before you begin to speak.

   Your own slow, relaxed speech will be far more effective than any criticism or advice such as "slow down" or "try it again slowly."

2. **Reduce the number of questions you ask your child.** Children speak more freely if they are expressing their own ideas rather than answering an adult's questions. Instead of asking questions, simply comment on what your child has said, thereby letting him know you heard him.

3. **Use your facial expressions and other body language to convey to your child** that you are listening to the content of her message and not to how she's talking.

4. **Set aside a few minutes at a regular time each day when you can give your undivided attention to your child.** During this time, let the child choose what he would like to do. Let him direct you in activities and decide himself whether to talk or not. When you talk during this special time, use slow, calm, and relaxed speech, with plenty of pauses.

   This quiet, calm time can be a confidence-builder for younger children, letting them know that a parent enjoys their company. As the child gets older, it can be a time when the child feels comfortable talking about his feelings and experiences with a parent.

5. **Help all members of the family learn to take turns talking and listening.** Children, especially those who stutter, find it much easier to talk when there are few interruptions and they have the listeners' attention.

6. **Observe the way you interact with your child.** Try to increase those times that give your child the message that you are listening to her and she has plenty of time to talk. Try to decrease criticisms, rapid speech patterns, interruptions, and questions.

7. **Above all, convey that you accept your child as he is.** The most powerful force will be your support of him, whether he stutters or not.

For more information on stuttering and ways to help your child, write or call the nonprofit...

Stuttering Foundation of America®
3100 Walnut Grove Road, Suite 603
P.O. Box 11749, Memphis, TN 38111-0749
1-800-992-9392 www.stutteringhelp.org

Additional Resources

We have compiled a list of resources on stuttering, teasing, and building self-esteem in children. This list is organized by intended audience: teachers, children, or parents. For a list of local and national support groups, please call The Stuttering Foundation.

For teachers:

Stuttering: For Kids, By Kids. Speech-language pathologists who specialize in the treatment of fluency disorders spent more than a year developing the script. The result is a lively, engaging and highly effective video that gives kids positive ways to manage their stuttering, boosts confidence and helps them feel better about themselves. A new and non-threatening way to discuss stuttering, #0160 and #0162.

Classroom Presentation Packet. This packet of materials contains cool tools to use when children make presentations to their class about stuttering. Thirty copies each of the *"16 Famous People Who Stutter: National Stuttering Awareness Week"* and *"Did You Know: Fact Sheet About Stuttering"* brochures; one *"16 Famous People Who Stutter"* poster and one *"Nick Brendon for National Stuttering Awareness Week"* poster are included. All materials are in full color. Order from The Stuttering Foundation, 1-800-992-9392 or www.stutteringhelp.org, #0130.

The Bully Free Classroom: Over 100 Tips and Strategies for Teachers K-8, by A. L. Beane. More than 100 practical strategies for prevention and intervention with teasing and bullying that can be used immediately can be found in this book. It includes 45 pages of reproducible handout masters. Order from Free Spirit Publishing, 1-800-735-7323 or www.amazon.com.

If Your Child Stutters: A Guide for Parents, 6th edition. Written for those who are concerned about the speech of the young child, this book helps distinguish between normal disfluencies and stuttering and offers practical suggestions parents can use immediately with their child. Many experts in the field of stuttering contributed to the book. Order from The Stuttering Foundation, 1-800-992-9392 or www.stutteringhelp.org, #0011.

Stuttering and Your Child: Questions and Answers, 3rd edition. This book represents the most up-to-date thoughts of seven leading authorities in stuttering. Answers to questions most often asked by parents enable them to work with their child in ways that contribute to the development of better fluency. This book is a must for both parents and teachers. Order from The Stuttering Foundation, 1-800-992-9392 or www.stutteringhelp.org, #0022.

Therapy in Action: The School-Age Child Who Stutters. This 40-minute video provides information about what stuttering looks and sounds like, concerns associated with stuttering in the school-age child, and therapy in action by renowned specialists with school-age children. Order from The Stuttering Foundation, 1-800-992-9392 or www.stutteringhelp.org, #0079.

Stuttering and the Bilingual Child. This brochure explains the unique demands being bilingual places on the stuttering child, and offers suggestions for reducing language demands as well as ideas for structuring therapy. Order from The Stuttering Foundation, 1-800-992-9392 or www.stutteringhelp.org, #0110.

16 Famous People Who Stutter Poster. Sixteen noted celebrities who stutter in full color. Nicholas Brendon, James Earl Jones, Annie Glenn, John Stossel, Kenyon Martin, Marilyn Monroe, Bob Love, Mel Tillis, Bill Walton, Carly Simon, King George VI, Frank Wolf, Ken Venturi, John Updike, Robert Merrill, Winston Churchill. 24" x 18". Ideal for all settings to increase awareness about stuttering. Order from The Stuttering Foundation, 1-800-992-9392 or www.stutteringhelp.org, #0054.

Nick Brendon for National Stuttering Awareness Week Poster. As "Xander" in the popular TV series, "Buffy the Vampire Slayer," Nicholas Brendon has won fans of all ages. This poster is ideal for classrooms and clinics. 12" x 18" Order from The Stuttering Foundation, 1-800-992-9392 or www.stutteringhelp.org, #0007.

For children:

Stuttering: For Kids, By Kids. In this new 12-minute video and DVD for kids, the animated character Swish talks to his real friends about their stuttering, asking such questions as, "Does stuttering ever bug you?" Children of various ages answer, sharing different views about: dealing with teasing; how to teach others about stuttering; and what helps them manage their stuttering.

Sometimes I Just Stutter, a book for ages 7 to 12, by E. de Geus. Written for children who stutter, this book talks about what makes you stutter, why sometimes you stutter and sometimes you don't, why some people don't understand why you stutter, what others know about stuttering, that a lot of other kids stutter too, and what to do if you are teased about stuttering. Order from The Stuttering Foundation, 1-800-992-9392 or www.stutteringhelp.org, #0031 or download from the Foundation's Web site for free. Also available in Spanish (item #0032).

Do You Stutter: A Guide for Teens, 3rd edition. Some problems are unique to teens who stutter. This 80-page book is written to and for teens to offer advice on solving some of these problems. Each chapter is written by a specialist in the field of stuttering, some who have stuttered. Order from The Stuttering Foundation, 1-800-992-9392 or www.stutteringhelp.org, #0021.

Stuttering: Straight Talk for Teens. Every teen needs to know that he or she is not alone, and that real help is available. In this newly updated 30-minute video, teens share experiences and talk about what works. Clinicians demonstrate and discuss what stuttering is, concerns and feelings associated with stuttering, and ways the teen can help himself and where to find help. Order from The Stuttering Foundation, 1-800-992-9392 or www.stutteringhelp.org, #0076.

I'm Like You, You're Like Me: A Child's Book About Understanding and Celebrating Each Other, by C. Gainer. Simple words and cute illustrations help children ages 3-8 discover and celebrate individual differences on their level: hair, families, body shapes, etc. Topics explored in basic terms include talking, listening, feelings, and cooperation. Order from Free Spirit Publishing, 1-800-735-7323 or www.amazon.com.

We Can Get Along: A Child's Book of Choices, by L. M. Payne & C. Rohling. For children ages 3-8, this book teaches conflict resolution and peacemaking skills in a way that young children can understand. Order from Free Spirit Publishing, 1-800-735-7323 or www.amazon.com. A Leader's Guide can also be ordered that includes activities, discussion questions, and reproducible handouts for parents.

Bullies Are a Pain in the Brain, by T. Romain. This book mixes humor with practical suggestions to help children ages 8-13 become "bully-proof," get help in dangerous situations, and stop bullies from hurting others. Information for bullies is also included to help them get along with others and feel good about themselves without having to make others feel bad. Order from Free Spirit Publishing, 1-800-735-7323 or www.amazon.com.

Stick Up For Yourself! Every Kid's Guide to Personal Power and Positive Self-Esteem, revised, by G. Kaufman, L. Raphael, & P. Espeland. Written for children in grades 3-7, this book contains simple words with real-life examples to help children build self-esteem, assertiveness skills, responsibility, and healthy relationships. Order from Free Spirit Publishing, 1-800-735-7323 or www.amazon.com. A Teacher's Guide is also available for this book with outlines for ten sessions and including reproducibles.

Stress Can Really Get on Your Nerves!, by T. Romain & E. Verdick. Blending facts, reassurance, and humor, this book written for children ages 8-13 helps them understand and manage their stress. It offers specific ways to deal with stress. Order from Free Spirit Publishing, 1-800-735-7323 or www.amazon.com.

Fighting Invisible Tigers: A Stress Management Guide for Teens, revised, by E. Hipp. Written especially for teens in grades 6-12, the book is a wonderful resource of stress-management and life-management skills. Covers being assertive, building relationships, taking risks, making decisions, dealing with fears, using positive self-talk, and more. A "Self-Care for Tiger Bites" offers immediate "first aid" for teens who need fast stress relief. Order from Free Spirit Publishing, 1-800-735-7323 or www.amazon.com. A Leader's Guide can also be ordered that includes a step-by-step curriculum for 12 sessions and handout masters.

For parents

If Your Child Stutters: A Guide for Parents, 6th edition, 2005. Written for parents who are concerned about the speech of their young child, this book helps distinguish between normal disfluencies and stuttering and offers practical suggestions parents can use immediately with their child. Many experts in the field of stuttering contributed to the book. Order from The Stuttering Foundation, 1-800-992-9392 or www.stutteringhelp.org.

How to Talk So Kids Will Listen and Listen So Kids Will Talk, by A. Faber & E. Mazlish. This book describes a step-by-step approach to improving communication in the home. "Reminder" pages, helpful cartoons, and excellent exercises will improve parents' ability to talk and problem-solve with children. The suggestions are appropriate for teachers too. The tools provided are appropriate for children of all ages. Can be found in almost any bookstore or ordered from www.amazon.com.

Sticks and Stones: 7 Ways Your Child Can Deal with Teasing, Conflict, and Other Hard Times, by S. Cooper. This book helps parents of children ages 4-12 teach their children the verbal skills they need to defend against hurtful words others say to them. There are examples and sample scripts that help children learn how to speak up for themselves, shut down bullies, counter peer pressure, deal with fights, etc. Order from Free Spirit Publishing, 1-800-735-7323 or www.amazon.com.

Stuttering and Your Child: Questions and Answers, 3rd edition. This book represents the most up-to-date thoughts of seven leading authorities in stuttering. Answers to questions most often asked by parents enable them to work with their child in ways that contribute to the development of better fluency. A must for both parents and teachers. Order from The Stuttering Foundation, 1-800-992-9392 or www.stutteringhelp.org, #0022.

If You Think Your Child is Stuttering, New Tips for Parents. Updated in 2005, this popular brochure describes the difference between normal disfluencies and stuttering and offers 9 tips that parents can immediately use to help their child. Order from The Stuttering Foundation, 1-800-992-9392 or www.stutteringhelp.org, #0041.

Stuttering and the Preschool Child: Help for Families. This 30-minute videotape is for families of children who stutter. It focuses on helping families understand stuttering and make changes to promote more fluent speech. Order from The Stuttering Foundation, 1-800-992-9392 or www.stutteringhelp.org, #0070. Also available in Spanish (#0072) and DVD, #0073.

Stuttering and Your Child: A Videotape for Parents. This 30 minute VHS videotape is for parents, teachers, day care professionals, and all those wanting to help the child who stutters. It discusses what stuttering is, what is thought to cause and worsen childhood stuttering, and what parents can do to help their child. Order from The Stuttering Foundation, 1-800-992-9392 or www.stutteringhelp.org, #0075.

Therapy In Action: The School-Age Child Who Stutters. This 40-minute video provides information about what stuttering looks and sounds like, concerns associated with stuttering in the school-age child, and therapy in action by renowned specialists with school-age children. Order from The Stuttering Foundation, 1-800-992-9392 or www.stutteringhelp.org, #0079.

Stuttering: Straight Talk for Teens. Every teen needs to know that he or she is not alone, and that real help is available. In this newly updated 30-minute video, teens share experiences and talk about what works. Clinicians demonstrate and discuss what stuttering is, concerns and feelings associated with stuttering, and ways the teen can help himself and where to find help. Order from The Stuttering Foundation, 1-800-992-9392 or www.stutteringhelp.org, #0076.

Good Friends are Hard to Find: Help Your Child Find, Make, and Keep Friends, by F. Frankel. A step-by-step guide for parents of children ages 5-12, that shows them how to help their children make friends and deal with other kids. Includes suggestions for dealing with teasing, bully, and meanness whether the child is the one being teased or the one who is teasing. Order from Free Spirit Publishing, 1-800-735-7323 or www.amazon.com.

Did You Know...

- Over three million Americans stutter.

- Stuttering affects three to four times as many males as females.

- Approximately 5 percent of all children go through a period of stuttering that lasts six months or more. Three-quarters of those will recover by late childhood, leaving about 1% with a long-term problem.

- Exciting new research in the areas of genetics, neurology, child development, and family dynamics is shedding light on the possible causes of stuttering. As a result, we have made tremendous progress in the prevention of stuttering in young children.

- Studies show that people who stutter are as intelligent and well-adjusted as those who don't.

- People who stutter are often self-conscious about it and may let it determine the vocation they choose.

- No single method has proven to work for everyone, despite many reports of cures through new treatments, drugs or devices.

- Stuttering becomes an increasingly formidable problem in the teen years.

- A qualified clinician can help not only children but also teenagers, young adults and even older adults make significant progress toward fluency.

- Kenyon Martin, James Earl Jones, John Stossel, Annie Glenn, Bill Walton, Mel Tillis, Nicholas Brendon, Alan Rabinowitz, Robert Merrill, Carly Simon, Ken Venturi, Bob Love, John Updike, Lewis Carroll, King George VI, Winston Churchill and Marilyn Monroe—all famous people who stutter.

Basketball star **Kenyon Martin** has been a two-time member of basketball's Team USA and was selected to the 2004 NBA All-Star Team.

20/20's **John Stossel** still struggles with stuttering, yet has become one of the most successful reporters in broadcast journalism today.

NBA All Star and H
Bill Walton is recogı
known NBC Sports ‹

As "Xander" in the popular TV series, *Buffy the Vampire Slayer*, **Nicholas Brendon** has won fans of all ages.

Bob Love, legendary star of the Chicago Bulls, now heads up Community Affairs for the championship team.

Annie Glenn, wife o
John Glenn, was grou
by a stuttering proble
therapy, hard work ai
helped to turn it arou

Explorer, conservationist, and zoologist **Alan Rabinowitz** works tirelessly to protect endangered species as described in his new book, *Beyond the Last Village*.

Robert Merrill, world-famous baritone, was the first American to sing 500 performances with the Metropolitan Opera.

Congressman **Frank Wolf** of Vir
feels that meeting the challenge
stuttering helped prepare him to
other challenges in life.

Singer Carly Simon, winner of an Oscar and a Grammy, not only has many hit records but is also an author of children's books.

Winston Churchill captured the attention of millions during WWII with his inspiring speeches.

Actor **James Earl Jones,** a Broadway and television star, is well-known for his voice as "Darth Vader" in *Star Wars* and his book, *Voices and Silences*.

Country music star and recording artist **Mel Tillis** has entertained audiences across the country and around the world.

Author **John Updike** continues his successful career with best-sellers *Rabbit at Rest* and *Brazil*.

Legendary golfer **Ken Venturi**, U.S. Open champion, is a successful commentator for CBS Sports.

Marilyn Monroe captivated movie audiences and fellow performers alike throughout her legendary career.

If you stutter, you are definitely in **good company!**

Section II

For Speech-Language Pathologists

This tape was developed to give teachers practical information about stuttering with two audiences in mind:

- teachers who will view it independently, and
- speech-language pathologists (SLPs) who will use the tape to inform teachers about stuttering.

It could also be used with administrators, support staff in the school, and parents as well as other kids. Keep in mind when sharing it with other audiences that it directly addresses the classroom teacher. You may want to photocopy parts of this *Handbook* for those who will be viewing the tape.

You will find a suggested inservice format and tips for using the tape for either a large group presentation or for an individual teacher meeting. Implement only those that best fit your work setting.

We also include a list of discussion questions for use in either a large group or individual meeting. A rationale for asking each question is included.

Next are guidelines for making a classroom presentation about stuttering. The Stuttering Foundation has a Classroom Presentation Packet with brochures, information, and posters you and the child can use.

You will find a list of professional resources on stuttering at the end of this booklet.

Large Group Inservice Outline and Tips

This 20-minute tape was designed for use as part of a brief inservice, ranging anywhere from 30-45 minutes. We encourage you to modify the suggestions for content to best suit your staff's needs.

I. Introduction (5 minutes)

A. State your personal interest in children who stutter and your goals for the inservice.

B. Provide an overview of the tape's content and length. It may be helpful to suggest that teachers write down one or two things they did NOT know about stuttering as they are watching; this can provide a spring-board for discussion after the tape ends.

C. Even though teachers may not currently have a child who stutters in their classroom, they may meet someone who stutters in public. In this case, it is helpful to orient teachers to the number of children who stutter in the building, or the number of adults who stutter in the United States.

II. View the tape (20 minutes)

III. Discussion (10-20 minutes, depending on the number of questions and group interaction)

A. Ask for general reactions to the tape.

B. Ask teachers to share one or two pieces of information that were new to them or feelings that the children expressed that were surprising to them.

C. If you have time, select several questions from the list in this booklet and facilitate a discussion. Keep in mind that any question you ask, along with your reaction to the person's answer, has the potential to put them "on the spot." Your skill in choosing which questions to ask and then facilitating an open, honest, and respectful interaction will determine the success of the discussion.

D. At the end of the inservice, restate your goals, summarize what was learned, and thank the group for attending.

Tips for Leading Large Group Discussions

You may need to repeat a question or someone's answer for the whole group so that everyone is able to hear it. This is especially important if the group is large or you're in a room with poor acoustics.

Periodically summarize what the group is sharing. This helps them stay focused and reorients them to what is being shared. For example,

"Mrs. Turner's idea about how she managed oral reports with her child really stimulated discussion. I believe we agreed that X, Y, and Z are important factors to consider when dealing with this issue."

If you have worked with a teacher in the past who had a child who stutters in his or her classroom, you might ask that teacher to share about the experience. One good way to ask him or her to do this is to first make a positive observation about that teacher.

"Last year Mrs. Clark had Timmy X in her classroom. One strategy I know Timmy found helpful was that before the lesson, she told the children what order she would be calling on them. I think that really helped Timmy anticipate when he was going to be called on. Mrs. Clark, what else do you think was helpful to Timmy?"

Accept all responses equally, even if you don't agree with them. If you do disagree and think that the point needs elaboration, wait a bit and discuss several other topics, then summarize and ask for other possible perspectives. For example:

"So far, we've discussed oral reports, teasing, and encouraging children who stutter to talk more in our classrooms. We've had several different points of view expressed on these topics. Let's go back to oral reports, where one suggestion was to always require students to give reports in front of the class as a way of overcoming fear. Does anyone else have any thoughts about or experiences with this that they'd like to share?"

Also, use I statements when you respond. That way, the person who offered an idea you disagreed with is less likely to feel defensive because you keep the content of your response focused on you rather than the other person.

"I think it's important for us to discuss this a bit more because I have had this same issue with other children and I'm not always sure how to handle it. I'm wondering how others of you feel about this. Certainly, you all have more experience with managing students who have to give oral reports, and I know many other children have to be afraid of this experience. How have you handled other children who were afraid?"

If someone asks for advice, use a counter-question (e.g., "Hm, that's a good question. How do you think teasing should be handled?") or direct the question to the group-at-large. This will elicit more information from the person asking for advice and offer the opportunity for collaborative problem solving.

Encourage brainstorming and problem solving by all members of the group. Ask them to draw on their own experiences with children who have faced similar situations; while not all children stutter, many children are afraid to participate in class for one reason or another, are teased, or appear to be "different" from their peers. Teachers are used to dealing with many of these situations on a daily basis and have a wealth of experiences from which to draw.

Tips for Meeting with Individual Teachers

If a teacher has referred a student to you because of concerns about stuttering, a brief questionnaire may be useful in gathering initial background information about the child. One questionnaire we like to use can be found on page 40. In it the teacher is asked to respond to ten open-ended statements:

- Some things I have noticed about this child's communication are...
- When this child answers questions in class, he/she...
- When this child speaks to me at my desk, he/she...
- When this child reads aloud, he/she...
- If/When this child has difficulty speaking, I respond by...
- If/When this child has difficulty speaking, other children respond by...
- If/When this child has difficulty speaking, it occurs mostly when...
- My knowledge about stuttering is...
- Other concerns I have about this child's success in the classroom are...
- Most importantly, right now I need to know...

At any point during therapy, an important part of the process is meeting personally with the teacher of a child who stutters. You may choose to give the teacher the *Straight Talk for Teachers* video to view before you meet with him or her, or view it together at the meeting as a means of providing information about stuttering.

Afterwards, a discussion may successfully address specific issues related that child's particular needs. Discuss the teacher's observations and concerns and help him or her understand the important role that teachers play in the therapy process.

- Before you meet with the teacher, be sure to talk with the child about what he or she thinks might help in the classroom.
- Let the teacher know that her observations are *very* important to the child's treatment.
- Ask questions related to the child's performance in the classroom, such as:
  - What situations in your classroom require successful oral participation?
  - In which situations have you observed this child speaking freely (e.g., raising his hand, being willing to share and participate)?
  - In which situations have you observed fluent speech? Stuttered speech?
  - When the child stutters, what do you observe him doing? (e.g., tense his lips, repeat words, look away, etc.)

    - Has the child ever talked about stuttering with you?
- Give the teacher specific information about the child's speech.
    - When the child's stuttering began;
    - What kind of things he does when he stutters;
    - How he thinks and feels about it.

- Understand the teacher's perspective and point of view.
    - What has her experience been with individuals who stutter?
    - What kinds of things has she already done that seem to be helpful?

- Talk about what you are working on in therapy.
    - Names of the tools
    - How they sound and what they look like

- Don't overwhelm teachers with information and suggestions. Try to give one or two practical ideas she can begin implementing right away, based on her most pressing concerns.

- Consider involving the child in a meeting with you and the teacher. Cover topics such as what the child wants her teacher to know about her stuttering and model the various skills learned in therapy for the teacher.

Possible Discussion Questions

The following questions could be used to stimulate discussion in either a large-group inservice or individual teacher meeting. The list of questions is not exhaustive nor is it in any particular order.

Following each question is a rationale for asking it. Choose several questions that are consistent with topics you want to bring up as part of your goals for the inservice or individual meeting.

Presenting any of these questions may be easiest in a large group because the group at large will often discuss the answers teachers give. In an individual meeting, a teacher might think that you are asking a question to put him or her "on the spot" and thus feel threatened. As a result, you must rely on your knowledge of the teacher, the child, the situation, and your intuition as you proceed.

Question 1: How do you feel when you hear a child stutter?

Rationale: Our feelings about listening to stuttering will affect how we respond and interact with the child. It's common for people, including SLPs, to feel uncomfortable when they hear someone stutter. Many times listeners don't know what to say or how to react. Allowing people to express these feelings in a safe environment is a good starting point in helping listeners feel "comfortable" talking with people who stutter.

For tips on how teachers can react to children who stutter, refer to the *Handbook for Teachers* accompanying this video. This information is addressed in the answer to the first question in the section entitled, "Questions Teachers May Have."

Question 2: How do you react verbally/physically when you hear a child stuttering?

Rationale: Reactions to children who stutter can make the child more or less comfortable. As noted, it is common to feel some level of discomfort when hearing someone stutter. Although we want to respond in appropriate ways to the child, our level of discomfort can unconsciously lead us to respond in a less than helpful manner such as physically tensing up, looking away or trying to complete a word or sentence for the child. These responses may lead the child to feel "cut off," rejected, or ignored. Give teachers an opportunity to discuss these different ways to react to stuttering. This in turn will help both them and the child to feel more comfortable.

Question 3: What role as a teacher do you think you should play with the child who stutters?

Rationale: Information teachers share in response to this question will help clarify how the teacher might support the therapy process. Remember that teachers have an enormous task in working with a highly diverse population of children and that tremendous demands are placed on teachers to support and teach children of many different needs. When faced with a child with yet another problem, such as stuttering, some teachers may feel overwhelmed.

In using a discussion question like this, you can discover what the teacher may be thinking and feeling and then help her to see that the child who stutters does not have to be treated in radically different ways. Use the video to build understanding of stuttering, then offer a few common sense interaction styles she may already use with others.

Question 4: What role do you think the parents of a child who stutters should play?

Rationale: The answer to this question will help clarify what the teacher's expectations are for the parents. Teachers may have preconceived ideas regarding the role of the parent, not only in the origins of stuttering but also in how it should be treated. We want to help build a healthy relationship between teacher and parent.

Allowing the teacher the opportunity to voice preconceived ideas of the parents' role in a safe non-judgmental atmosphere gives you insight on how you can proceed with the teacher and parents. What attitudes are helpful and should be reinforced? What beliefs need to be modified in a safe, non-threatening manner?

Question 5: What is the role of the SLP in working with the child who stutters?

Rationale: When you raise this question, it gives you the opportunity to hear exactly what the teacher may expect of you, and gives you the chance to respond in a supportive, non-threatening way even if your perception of your role is not the same teacher's.

This can lead to an open, sharing discussion about what the various roles might be for both teacher and SLP. It also provides the SLP the opportunity to give teachers more specifics about stuttering therapy. Both concepts are important for the development and implementation of the IEP.

Question 6: What has your experience been with individuals who stutter?

Rationale: It's critical to understand teachers' experience with and knowledge about stuttering. Their responses will enable you to determine whether you need to provide them with a more complete picture of stuttering, and the wide variety of behaviors, attitudes, and feelings among children who stutter.

Questions 7 & 8: What have you done with other children who stutter that you found to be helpful? Have you had experiences where what you have done was NOT helpful?

Rationale: This allows you to validate what the teacher has already done and make suggestions for more helpful strategies if necessary. We want teachers to share previous interactions with children who stutter. You can discuss the various examples the teachers provide, decide if they were indeed helpful, and problem-solve other strategies. Further questions you may want to ask include: Would the things you've done be helpful to all children who stutter? If not, how could the strategy be modified to work better with select children?

Question 9: How did this video increase your understanding of stuttering and of children who stutter?

Rationale: It's important to determine whether you need to provide more information about stuttering; therefore, this is a good closing question. At this point, teachers will have talked about issues, and learned strategies that may make them feel more comfortable or increase the success of their interactions with children who stutter. You can also gain a sense of whether additional information needs to be presented immediately for the benefit of the group or discussed with individual teachers at a later date.

Guidelines for Classroom Presentations for Children Who Stutter:

(adapted with permission from Murphy, 2002)

Having the school-aged child and SLP discuss stuttering with the child's class is a powerful tool with many positive consequences. When classmates are informed about the nature of stuttering, teasing in the classroom is almost always reduced or eliminated. Classmates also become advocates for the child who stutters and will come to his rescue on the playground if other children tease him.

A class presentation is one way to normalize, "de-awfulize" stuttering. When done correctly, the stuttering is a less "loaded" topic, an issue that can be openly discussed. It opens the possibility that the SLP can go directly into the classroom and work openly with the child on transfer and maintenance skills. If appropriate, teachers can more easily signal a child to use his management tools.

Most importantly, the child has a powerful experience during which there is opportunity to self-disclose about stuttering in a supportive and accepting environment. He can implement therapy strategies in class without worrying about potential misunderstanding or ridicule by others. Thus, the foundation is laid to use self-disclosure as a stuttering management tool. The child learns that talking openly about stuttering puts both him and peers at ease.

Procedures for Making a Classroom Presentation

A classroom presentation to help a child discuss his stuttering with his classmates should be done **only if the child is in agreement. Not all children who stutter are ready or willing to make a classroom presentation to their peers.** Deciding to make a presentation should be viewed as a therapy goal for how the child thinks and feels about the problem, and the child's readiness for this activity should be monitored carefully.

For some children, making this decision is an easy task. They want their classmates to know about stuttering. For others who have been teased about stuttering or who already have strong negative emotions, desensitization work must come first. Strategies to reduce or eliminate anxiety, shame, and guilt must be implemented both in and outside the therapy room. (Editor's note: For therapy suggestions, see SFA video #0086, *The School-age Child Who Stutters: Dealing Effectively with Shame and Guilt,* or SFA book #0005, *The School-age Child Who Stutters: Working Effectively with Attitudes & Emotions–A Workbook.*)

Explain the rationale for this experience to teachers and parents. Even if a child has not been teased about stuttering by classmates, he will acquire important skills.

During a conference with the teacher, the general mood of the classroom is discussed to determine whether the teacher expects interference from any particular child.

The child who stutters should be included in those planning activities. Does he want to inform the class regarding specific issues? How much does he want to actually say versus what the SLP should say? If he is still at a point where speech management skills are inconsistent, the SLP may want to limit the child's participation to speaking parts that are short, well-rehearsed, or use strategies known to produce a lot of fluency, such as choral reading.

Issues discussed will vary according to each child's needs and age level. kindergarten, first, and second-grade children can understand concepts of bumpy or sticky speech and that it feels bad to be teased. They can learn that the speech teacher will teach the child who stutters how to have smoother speech, but that sometimes bumpy speech will still happen.

Third and fourth graders can understand more complex explanations about stuttering, how speech is produced, speech therapy techniques, their inconsistent success, and the ramifications of teasing.

Here is sample outline of a classroom presentation that would be appropriate for third and fourth graders. You will want to adapt it to your own style, the needs of the child in question, and the developmental level of the class.

Classroom Presentation Outline

1. Introduction
   - Introduce yourself as the speech teacher and briefly explain your job.
2. Classroom participation.
   - To normalize the concept of receiving speech therapy in the classroom, ask the children how many of them have been to speech before and what they worked on.
   - Maybe someone will mention that the child who stutters is currently in speech. Acknowledge that this is true and soon you'll be discussing it.
3. Talk about other speech problems and the rationale for coming to class.
   - Briefly indicate that there are many types of speech difficulties, e.g., how to pronounce speech sounds, hoarse voices etc., but today you and the child are going to focus on a problem called stuttering.

- Let the class know that you and the child want to teach them some interesting things about stuttering and to educate them, because we all know how important it is to be educated people.

4. Define stuttering and its causation.
   - Give a brief definition that is age appropriate for the class.
   - When speaking to this age level, we like to ask the kids if they know what stuttering is and summarize the discussion with something like, "Stuttering is a speech problem where some people's speech system doesn't work very well all the time. It doesn't seem to be as coordinated as it should. It gets tripped up or stuck on sounds. We're not sure what causes this but we think maybe some people are just born this way."
5. Famous people who stutter.
   - We like to ask the class if they know that many famous and successful people have stuttered and then briefly tell them about some of these people, pictured in the centerfold in this booklet (pages 20-21).
   - As a visual aid, you can use the brochure enclosed in this packet showing famous people who stutter.
6. It's no one's fault.
   - It's very important to stress that no one is responsible for stuttering. People don't stutter because they are dumb or sick. Moms and Dads did not cause it and it's not a disease that you can catch.
7. Different ways to stutter.
   - Most children, no matter what their degree of speech management skill, can be verbally involved with the class in this portion of the presentation.
   - Together with the child, demonstrate different forms of stuttering behavior (e.g., repetitions, blocks).
   - Ask for volunteers to imitate the various patterns. It can be fun, if done in a friendly manner, for the child who stutters to grade stuttering attempts by classmates (i.e., give them an A, B, C, D, or F).
   - Indicate that this type of imitation is for learning purposes only and that it should not be done at other times.
   - A class discussion should then follow in which the children are asked how they would feel and act if they had to talk this way all of the time.
8. Tools that facilitate smoother speech.
   - Using the linguistic level at which the child is most comfortable, together you can demonstrate the speech management techniques he or she is learning, e.g., pullouts, stretched speech, etc.

- It may also be helpful to ask a few of the other children in the class if they can do some of the fluency enhancing techniques, such as prolonged speech. Here the class may begin to appreciate the level of difficulty in using such management techniques.

9. We can't have 100% success – change is hard!
   - It's important that both the teacher and the class recognize that speech management in conversation is difficult and the child will continue to have some hard stuttering. Change will come, but it takes time and practice.
   - Influences that make changes difficult can be discussed. Items may vary for each child but usually include the following: being tired, competing messages (i.e., many children trying to talk at once), and fear of being teased or ridiculed.
10. Why people make fun of others and how it affects us.
    - Ask the class to share what they have been teased about. Most elementary-aged children are willing to disclose this information and doing so actually creates a stronger bond among the children.
    - We always emphasize that anyone who is willing to share something they have been teased about is very brave.
    - It is also helpful to ask the children how teasing makes them feel and act.
    - Parallels can then be drawn to teasing someone about stuttering.
    - Help the children problem solve various ways they can respond if they hear one of their classmates being teased or bullied.
11. How the child would like his classmates to respond to stuttering.
    - You and the child can talk to the class about how to react to stuttering in a helpful manner.
    - We have found that many elementary children actually welcome their classmates filling in words on which they are stuttering, while others want the listener to be patient and wait until they are able to say the word.

Appropriate discussions and self-disclosure of stuttering take the disorder out of the closet. It can take the sting out of "a secret that everyone knows but no one talks about," thus reducing shame, fear, and mystery. Self-disclosure and other forms of desensitization must be done repetitively but in safe, socially appropriate contexts such as classroom presentations, plays, or child-directed videos about stuttering.

Additional Resources

We have compiled a list of resources on stuttering therapy, teasing, and building self-esteem in children. This list is organized by intended audience: speech-language pathologists, teachers, children, or parents. Also see page 41 for a helpful parent questionnaire. It includes 10 open-ended statements to obtain parents' perception about the stuttering. You may also call The Stuttering Foundation at 1-800-992-9392 for a list of support groups.

For speech-language pathologists:

Classroom Presentation Packet. This packet of materials contains cool tools to use when children make presentations to their class about stuttering. Thirty copies each of the *"16 Famous People Who Stutter: National Stuttering Awareness Week"* and *"Did You Know: Fact Sheet About Stuttering"* brochures; one *"16 Famous People Who Stutter"* poster and one *"Nick Brendon for National Stuttering Awareness Week"* poster are included. All materials are in full color. Order from The Stuttering Foundation, 1-800-992-9392 or www.stutteringhelp.org, #0130.

Stuttering: For Kids, By Kids. Speech-language pathologists who specialize in the treatment of fluency disorders spent more than a year developing the script. The result is a lively, engaging and highly effective video that gives kids positive ways to manage their stuttering, boosts confidence and helps them feel better about themselves. A new and non-threatening way to discuss stuttering.

Working with Teachers: Practical Ideas for School Clinicians, by A. McKeehan and K. Chmela. Well-known speech pathologists Ann McKeehan and Kristin Chmela share practical ideas and strategies for working with classroom teachers to meet the needs of children who stutter in this 40-minute video. Tips for inservicing teachers are offered by McKeehan; Chmela addresses collaborating with teachers to achieve transfer and maintenance of fluency skills. A handout accompanies the tape. Order from The Stuttering Foundation, 1-800-992-9392 or www.stutteringhelp.org, #0102.

Treating the School-Age Child Who Stutters: A Guide for Clinicians, 2nd edition by C. Dell. Written by a former public school SLP who was one of the first to be trained as a stuttering specialist, this 108-page book offers sample dialogues and numerous tools for working effectively with school-age children who stutter. A must for any public school speech-language pathologist working with elementary-aged children Order from The Stuttering Foundation, 1-800-992-9392 or www.stutteringhelp.org, #0014.

Therapy in Action: The School-Age Child Who Stutters. This 40-minute video provides information about what stuttering looks and sounds like, concerns associated with stuttering in the school-age child, and segments of therapy in action by renowned specialists with school-age children. Order from The Stuttering Foundation, 1-800-992-9392 or www.stutteringhelp.org, #0079.

The School-Age Child who Stutters: Working Effectively with Attitudes and Emotions—A Workbook, by K. Chmela and N. Reardon. Numerous strategies for helping children make positive changes in feelings and beliefs are presented using examples from real children. Concrete methods for documenting present levels of feelings and beliefs are included, as well as therapy ideas to promote change. There are reproducible pages throughout the book. Order from The Stuttering Foundation, 1-800-992-9392 or www.stutteringhelp.org, #0005.

16 Famous People Who Stutter Poster. Sixteen noted celebrities who stutter in full color. Nicholas Brendon, James Earl Jones, Annie Glenn, John Stossel, Marilyn Monroe, Bob Love, Mel Tillis, Bill Walton, Carly Simon, King George VI, Frank Wolf, Ken Venturi, John Updike, Robert Merrill, Winston Churchill. 24" x 18". Ideal for all settings to increase awareness about stuttering. Order from The Stuttering Foundation, 1-800-992-9392 or www.stutteringhelp.org, #0054.

Nick Brendon for National Stuttering Awareness Week Poster. As "Xander" in the popular TV series, "Buffy the Vampire Slayer," Nicholas Brendon has won fans of all ages. This poster is ideal for classrooms and clinics. 12" x 18" Order from The Stuttering Foundation, 1-800-992-9392 or www.stutteringhelp.org, #0007.

In addition, articles from several professional journals may be of interest:

- Logan, K. & Yaruss, J. S. (1999). Helping parents address attitudinal and emotional factors with young children who stutter. *Contemporary Issues in Communication Sciences & Disorders,* 26, 69-81.
- Zebrowski, P. M. (2002). Building clinical relationships with teenagers who stutter. *Contemporary Issues in Communication Sciences & Disorders,* 29, 91-100.
- Zebrowski, P. M., & Cilek, T. (1997). Stuttering therapy in the elementary school setting: Guidelines for clinician-teacher collaboration. *Seminars in Speech and Language,* 18, 329-341.
- Zebrowski, P. M. & Schum, R. L. (1993). Counseling parents of children who stutter. *American Journal of Speech-Language Pathology,* 2, 65-73.

For teachers:

Stuttering: For Kids, By Kids. Speech-language pathologists who specialize in the treatment of fluency disorders spent more than a year developing the script. The result is a lively, engaging and highly effective video that gives kids positive ways to manage their stuttering, boosts confidence and helps them feel better about themselves. A new and non-threatening way to discuss stuttering.

The Bully Free Classroom: Over 100 Tips and Strategies for Teachers K-8, by A. L. Beane. More than 100 practical strategies for prevention and intervention with teasing and bullying that can be used immediately can be found in this book. It includes 45 pages of reproducible handout masters. Order from Free Spirit Publishing, 1-800-735-7323 or www.amazon.com.

Stuttering and Your Child: Questions and Answers, 3rd edition. Updated in 2002, this book represents the most up-to-date thoughts of seven leading authorities in stuttering. Answers to questions most often asked by parents enable them to work with their child in ways that contribute to the development of better fluency. This book is a must for both parents and teachers. Order from The Stuttering Foundation, 1-800-992-9392 or www.stutteringhelp.org, #0022.

Therapy in Action: The School-Age Child Who Stutters. This 40-minute video provides information about what stuttering looks and sounds like, concerns associated with stuttering in the school-age child, and therapy in action by renowned specialists with school-age children. Order from The Stuttering Foundation, 1-800-992-9392 or www.stutteringhelp.org, #0079.

Stuttering and the Bilingual Child. This brochure explains the unique demands being bilingual places on the stuttering child, and offers suggestions for reducing language demands as well as ideas for structuring therapy. Order from The Stuttering Foundation, 1-800-992-9392 or www.stutteringhelp.org, #0110.

For children:

Stuttering: For Kids, By Kids. In this new 12-minute video and DVD for kids, the animated character Swish talks to his real friends about their stuttering, asking such questions as, "Does stuttering ever bug you?" Children of various ages answer, sharing different views about: dealing with teasing; how to teach others about stuttering; and what helps them manage their stuttering.

Sometimes I Just Stutter, a book for ages 7 to 12, by E. de Geus. Written for children who stutter, this book talks about what makes you stutter, why sometimes you stutter and sometimes you don't, why some people don't understand why you stutter, what others know about stuttering, that a lot of other kids stutter too, and what to do if you are teased about stuttering. Order from The Stuttering Foundation, 1-800-992-9392 or www.stutteringhelp.org, #0031. Also available in Spanish (item #0032).

Bullies Are a Pain in the Brain, by T. Romain. This book mixes humor with practical suggestions to help children ages 8-13 become "bully-proof," get help in dangerous situations, and stop bullies from hurting others. Information for bullies is also included to help them get along with others and feel good about themselves without having to make others feel bad. Order from Free Spirit Publishing, 1-800-735-7323 or www.amazon.com.

Stick Up For Yourself! Every Kid's Guide to Personal Power and Positive Self-Esteem, revised, by G. Kaufman, L. Raphael, & P. Espeland. Written for children in grades 3-7, this book contains simple words with real-life examples to help children build self-esteem, assertiveness skills, responsibility, and healthy relationships. Order from Free Spirit Publishing, 1-800-735-7323 or www.amazon.com. A Teacher's Guide is also available for this book with outlines for ten sessions including reproducibles.

Stress Can Really Get on Your Nerves!, by T. Romain & E. Verdick. Blending facts, reassurance, and humor, this book written for children ages 8-13 helps them understand and manage their stress. It offers specific ways to deal with stress. Order from Free Spirit Publishing, 1-800-735-7323 or www.amazon.com.

Fighting Invisible Tigers: A Stress Management Guide for Teens, revised, by E. Hipp. Written especially for teens in grades 6-12, the book is a wonderful resource of stress-management and life-management skills. Covers being assertive, building relationships, taking risks, making decisions, dealing with fears, using positive self-talk, and more. A "Self-Care for Tiger Bites" offers immediate "first aid" for teens who need fast stress relief. Order from Free Spirit Publishing, 1-800-735-7323 or www.amazon.com. A Leader's Guide can also be ordered that includes a step-by-step curriculum for 12 sessions and handout masters.

Do You Stutter: A Guide for Teens, 3rd edition. Some problems are unique to teens who stutter. This 80-page book is written to and for teens to offer advice on solving some of these problems. Each chapter is written by a specialist in the field of stuttering, some who have stuttered. Order from The Stuttering Foundation, 1-800-992-9392 or www.stutteringhelp.org, #0021.

Stuttering: Straight Talk for Teens. Every teen needs to know that he or she is not alone, and that real help is available. In this newly updated 30-minute video, teens share experiences and talk about what works. Clinicians demonstrate and discuss what stuttering is, concerns and feelings associated with stuttering, and ways the teen can help himself and where to find help. Order from The Stuttering Foundation, 1-800-992-9392 or www.stutteringhelp.org, #0076.

I'm Like You, You're Like Me: A Child's Book About Understanding and Celebrating Each Other, by C. Gainer. Simple words and cute illustrations help children ages 3-8 discover and celebrate individual differences on their level: hair, families, body shapes, etc. Topics explored in basic terms include talking, listening, feelings, and cooperation. Order from Free Spirit Publishing, 1-800-735-7323 or www.amazon.com. A Leader's Guide can also be ordered that includes activities, discussion questions, and reproducible handouts for parents.

We Can Get Along: A Child's Book of Choices, by L. M. Payne & C. Rohling. For children ages 3-8, this book teaches conflict resolution and peacemaking skills in a way that young children can understand. Order from Free Spirit Publishing, 1-800-735-7323 or www.amazon.com. A Leader's Guide can also be ordered that includes activities, discussion questions, and reproducible handouts for parents.

For parents:

If Your Child Stutters: A Guide for Parents, 6th edition. Written for parents who are concerned about the speech of their young child, this book helps distinguish between normal disfluencies and stuttering and offers practical suggestions parents can use immediately with their child. Many experts in the field of stuttering contributed to the book. Order from The Stuttering Foundation, 1-800-992-9392 or www.stutteringhelp.org, #0011. Also available in Spanish (#0015).

Stuttering and Your Child: Questions and Answers, 3rd edition. This book represents the most up-to-date thoughts of seven leading authorities in stuttering. Answers to questions most often asked by parents enable them to work with their child in ways that contribute to the development of better fluency. A must for both parents and teachers. Order from The Stuttering Foundation, 1-800-992-9392 or www.stutteringhelp.org, #0022. Also available in Spanish (#0027).

If You Think Your Child is Stuttering, New Tips for Parents. This popular brochure describes the difference between normal disfluencies and stuttering and offers 9 tips that parents can immediately use to help their child. Order from The Stuttering Foundation, 1-800-992-9392 or www.stutteringhelp.org, #0041. Also available in Spanish (#0048).

Stuttering and the Preschool Child: Help for Families. This 30-minute videotape is for families of preschool children who stutter. It focuses on helping families understand stuttering and make changes to promote more fluent speech. Order from The Stuttering Foundation, 1-800-992-9392 or www.stutteringhelp.org, #0070. Also available in Spanish (#0072).

How to Talk So Kids Will Listen and Listen So Kids Will Talk, by A. Faber and E. Mazlish. This book describes a step-by-step approach to improving communication in the home. "Reminder" pages, helpful cartoons, and excellent exercises will improve parents' ability to talk and problem-solve with children. The suggestions are appropriate for teachers too. The tools provided are appropriate for children of all ages. Can be found in almost any bookstore or ordered from www.amazon.com.

Good Friends are Hard to Find: Help Your Child Find, Make, and Keep Friends, by F. Frankel. A step-by-step guide for parents of children ages 5-12, that shows them how to help their children make friends and deal with other kids. Includes suggestions for dealing with teasing, bully, and meanness whether the child is the one being teased or the one who is teasing. Order from Free Spirit Publishing, 1-800-735-7323 or www.amazon.com.

Sticks and Stones: 7 Ways Your Child Can Deal with Teasing, Conflict, and Other Hard Times, by S. Cooper. This book helps parents of children ages 4-12 teach their children the verbal skills they need to defend against hurtful words others say to them. There are examples and sample scripts that help children learn how to speak up for themselves, shut down bullies, counter peer pressure, deal with fights, etc. Order from Free Spirit Publishing, 1-800-735-7323 or www.amazon.com.

Stuttering and Your Child: A Videotape for Parents. This 30 minute VHS videotape is for parents, teachers, day care professionals, and all those wanting to help the child who stutters. It discusses what stuttering is, what is thought to cause and worsen childhood stuttering, and what parents can do to help their child. Order from The Stuttering Foundation, 1-800-992-9392 or www.stutteringhelp.org, #0075.

Therapy in Action: The School-Age Child Who Stutters. This 40-minute video provides information about what stuttering looks and sounds like, concerns associated with stuttering in the school-age child, and therapy in action by renowned specialists with school-age children. Order from The Stuttering Foundation, 1-800-992-9392 or www.stutteringhelp.org, #0079.

Stuttering: Straight Talk for Teens. Every teen needs to know that he or she is not alone, and that real help is available. In this newly updated 30-minute video, teens share experiences and talk about what works. Clinicians demonstrate and discuss what stuttering is, concerns and feelings associated with stuttering, and ways the teen can help himself and where to find help. Order from The Stuttering Foundation, 1-800-992-9392 or www.stutteringhelp.org, #0076.

Teacher Questionnaire

Name of Child: ____________________

Teacher: ____________________

Grade/Section: ____________________

Date: ____________________

Return form to: ____________________

Please complete the following statements:

1. Some things I have noticed about this child's communication are...

2. When this child answers questions in class, he/she...

3. When this child speaks to me at my desk, he/she...

4. When this child reads aloud, he/she...

5. If/When this child has difficulty speaking, I respond by...

6. If/When this child has difficulty speaking, other children respond by...

7. If/When this child has difficulty speaking, it occurs mostly when...

8. My knowledge about stuttering is...

9. Other concerns I have about this child's success in the classroom are...

10. Most importantly, right now I need to know...

ISBN 0-933388-49-7 / 800-992-9392
www.stutteringhelp.org

Parent Questionnaire

Name of Child: ______________________________

Name of Parent(s): ___________________________

Date: _______________________________________

Please complete the following statements:

1. My greatest concerns regarding my child's speech problem are...

2. I feel my child is/is not aware of his/her speech problem because...

3. I feel my child is/is not concerned about his/her speech problem because...

4. The situations where my child has the most trouble talking are...

5. When my child stutters, I feel...

6. When my child stutters, I say/do...

7. When my child stutters, other family members react by...

8. My knowledge about stuttering is...

9. From previous therapy, if any, I learned...

10. As a result of this therapy, I hope...

ISBN 0-933388-49-7 / 800-992-9392
www.stutteringhelp.org

If you believe this book has helped you or you wish to help this worthwhile cause, please send a donation to

THE
STUTTERING
FOUNDATION®

A Nonprofit Organization
Since 1947—Helping Those Who Stutter

3100 Walnut Grove Road, Suite 603
P.O. Box 11749 • Memphis, TN 38111-0749

1-800-992-9392

www.stutteringhelp.org www.tartamudez.org
info@stutteringhelp.org

The Stuttering Foundation of America® is a tax-exempt organization under section 501(c)(3) of the Internal Revenue Code and is classified as a private operating foundation as defined in section 4942(j)(3). Charitable contributions and bequests to the Foundation are tax-deductible, subject to limitations under the Code.